Love is the answer.
What was the question?

The way to
know life
is to
love
many things.
-Vincent Van Gogh

I have decided to stick with love.
Hate is too great a burden to bear. -Martin Luther King, Jr.

Love is not
an emotion,
it's your very existence.
-Rumi

I love those who can smile in trouble,
who can gather strength from distress,
and grow brave by reflection.
'Tis the business of little minds to shrink,
but they whose heart is firm,
and whose conscience approves their conduct,
will pursue their principles unto death.
-Leonardo da Vinci

Love is of all passions the strongest,
for it attacks simultaneously the head, the heart and the senses.
-Lao Tzu

Love
is the
greatest
refreshment
in life.
-Pablo Picasso

Hatred does not cease by hatred, but only by love; this is the eternal rule.  -Buddha

Only love interests me,
and I am only in contact
with things
that revolve around love.
-Marc Chagall

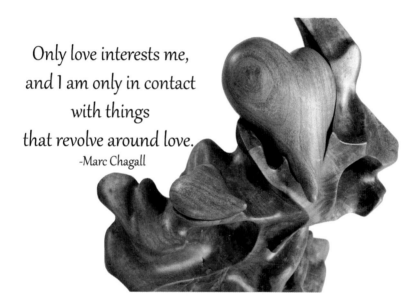

Love is a canvas
furnished by nature
and
embroidered
by
imagination.
-Voltaire

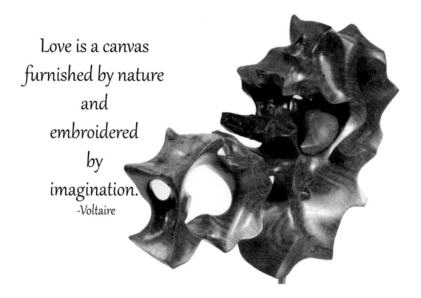

There is
no remedy
for love
but to
love more.
-Henry David Thoreau

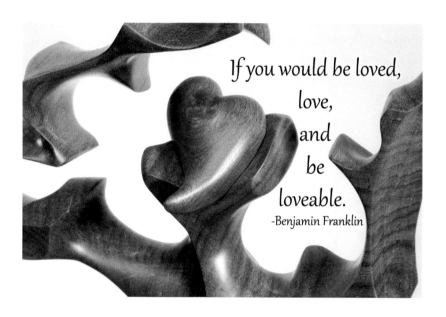

If you would be loved,
love,
and
be
loveable.
-Benjamin Franklin

A new command
I give you:
Love
one
another.

As I have loved you,
so you must
love
one
another.

-Jesus